Page 6

Page 10

W9-BQT-277

The Greenville Gazette

FIVE INFORMATIONAL TEXTS

by Rebecca Grudzina

Table of Contents

Informational Texts

What is an informational text?

Informational text is nonfiction text that presents information in an accurate and organized way. It is often about a single subject such as an event or time period in history or a scientific discovery. It may be about any topic, such as a sport or a hobby. The research report that you write for a school assignment is an informational text. So is an article you read in your favorite fashion magazine or on a Web site. A newspaper account of a local election and a history book chapter on a famous battle are additional examples of informational texts.

What is the purpose of informational texts?

Informational text has one main purpose: to inform. The best informational writing does this in a way that keeps readers' attention. It pulls readers in, making them want to keep reading and to know more about the topic.

How do you read an informational text?

When you read informational text, look for facts and for the details that support them. Read critically to make sure your conclusions make sense. If there is more than one way to look at an event or situation, make sure it is given. Ask yourself: *Did I learn something new from this text? Do I want to know more about it? Can I draw my own conclusions from what I have read?*

The information is accurate and the facts have been checked.

The text has a strong beginning that hooks the reader.

The text uses primary sources when appropriate.

Features of an Informational Text

The text has a strong ending that keeps readers thinking.

The information includes graphics that support the text.

The text includes multiple perspectives so that the reader can draw his or her own conclusions.

The text has a logical organization of major concepts.

Who writes informational texts?

Writers who know their topic well write good informational text. They do this by becoming mini-experts on the subjects they are writing about. They make sure that they support the information in their work with historical facts, scientific data, graphics like time lines and diagrams, and expert evidence. They provide more than one person's point of view. They use primary sources—firsthand information like journals and photographs.

Tools for Readers and Writers

A Strong Lead

A strong lead, or the first few sentences, grabs or "hooks" readers. A strong lead makes readers want to keep reading. The lead tells you something important about the subject and hints at what you may learn. Writers use two types of leads. A direct lead tells who or what the piece is about and why the subject is important. An indirect lead may quote someone, ask a question, describe a setting, or tell an anecdote, or true story, about the subject.

Advanced Nouns

Authors often choose nouns based on their audience. If an author is writing a children's book about a cat, she might use the noun **cat**. If she is writing a cat book aimed at intermediate students, she might use the noun **feline**. Good readers know to look for more advanced nouns while they are reading. Advanced nouns usually have more specific meanings and allow writers to be very precise. They also increase vocabulary and develop good writing skills.

Summarize Information

A summary is a brief retelling of the events of a story or article. To help readers remember what they have read, they summarize as they read. Good readers often write down important events and details as they read, keeping these notes short and to the point. Sometimes an important event is identified in one paragraph and developed through following paragraphs. Other times important events are never identified. Readers have to use what they read to figure out those unidentified events.

About Newspaper Reporting

Many people read newspapers every day to find out what is happening in their communities and the world. Some people read news in a printed paper; others read articles on the Internet. Some newspapers report stories from around the world, while other newspapers cover only local events in one community. Many schools have newspapers, too.

Newspapers often divide their stories into sections that have a particular theme. Some common sections include "News," "Sports," "Politics," "Lifestyle," "Crime," and "Travel." Inside each section is a mix of hard news stories and feature stories.

A hard news story contains information about something that is current. Often the reader needs to know the information to take an action. Stories about election results or crimes that took place the day before are examples of hard news. These articles are often short and written in a way that gives the most important information in the first few paragraphs. Following paragraphs elaborate on the topic.

A feature story is a detailed look into a specific topic. Features do not have to be current, but are usually published at a time when people would be interested in the topic (such as the history of the space program before a launch). Features tend to be written in a more narrative storytelling style.

Locker-Room Phantom Strikes Again

Steals Dozens of Shoes and Decorates Trees

Ms. Anderson's gym class had quite a surprise when they returned to their lockers after fourth period Thursday.

"All of our shoes were gone, the girls' and the boys'," said GHS ninth-grader Samantha Ruiz. "We left them under the benches when we put on our tennis sneakers, and when we came back to change they were all gone."

Fortunately, the students didn't have to go far to find them again. Outside the main entrance to the gymnasium, a tree was completely draped with shoes.

"They were hung there like decorations," Amar Kahn noted. "Ones without shoelaces were set on the ground around the tree."

The shoe **caper** is the most recent in a series of pranks pulled by the person known as the Locker-Room Phantom. Last month, Coach Wilson's football team returned from practice to find green food coloring in its water cooler. "It looked so gross," fullback Ryan Davidson said. "We were afraid to drink it so we dumped it out on the driveway. It made the driveway green, too."

Two months ago, the girls' volleyball team reported that all of the white towels had been tied in a bunch and stuck in one of the basketball hoops.

There have also been cases

The tree outside of the gym was covered with shoes
after the Locker-Room Phantom struck again.

of baseball bats hidden in showers and balls packed into closets to fall on the unlucky people who open them. Once, Sandra Ming, who dresses as the school **mascot**, found her eagle costume on a **mannequin** on the soccer field.

Sandra Ming's eagle costume had to be cleaned after
the Phantom left it overnight on the soccer field.

No one knows how the prankster pulls off the pranks without being seen. He or she often strikes when the victims are close by, in broad daylight. "I don't know how the prankster does it," Ms. Anderson said. "It's like he or she is invisible."

Principal Lakhi and the rest of the administrators are trying very hard to find the **culprit**. "These pranks are immature. They are destructive, and they could be dangerous. This prankster is a thief, and he or she must be punished."

Some members of the student body disagree. They say the pranks are funny. After his shoes were hung in the tree, Amar Kahn said he laughed. "At first I was mad my shoes were gone. But I got them back. Everyone did. And the sight of them on the tree was hilarious."

Sandra Ming had a different reaction. "It was really muddy that day, and my eagle costume got all dirty. Do you know how hard it is to clean an eagle costume?"

To stop the pranks, all of the gym teachers and the coaches will be taking turns monitoring the locker-room area. But to speed up the judicial process, Principal Lakhi is asking for all students to help. "If you know anything about these incidents, please tell your teacher. You will not be tattling; you will be helping us keep the gymnasium secure."

If you have any information about the prankster, contact your teacher or another member of the staff. If you wish to remain anonymous, leave a note. ❖

Rookie QB Leads Eagles to Finals

In a hair-raising fourth quarter, GHS newcomer Henry Malina led his fellow Eagles to a one-touchdown win over the Ravens. The victory puts the Eagles into the finals.

Henry Malina

The winning touchdown occurred just three seconds before the clock ran out, with the Eagles trailing by three points.

The game started poorly for the Eagles. Five seconds into the first play, the Ravens scored a touchdown and a two-point **conversion**. "We knew we were underdogs when we started," GHS Coach Christopher Wilson said, "but that really scared us."

The first half held nothing but disappointment for the Eagles. The Ravens intercepted their passes and kept our boys behind their fifty-yard line. Meanwhile, the Ravens racked up five more touchdowns for a staggering total of forty-three points.

"It was a very rough halftime," linebacker Andre Martin said. "We thought Coach would yell at us, but he just said to put the first half behind us and go out there fresh."

The GHS Eagles advanced to the state finals after last night's win against the Ravens.

Coach Wilson decided to give Malina a chance in the second half. "I thought, what did we have to lose? Henry is new to the team, but he has a good spirit. I wanted to see what he could do."

Before taking the field, Malina told his teammates that they had a chance only if they worked as a team. "One person cannot win a football game," Malina said. "We need to work together."

The team seemed to take that idea to heart, and in the third quarter they managed to score a whopping five touchdowns. Malina himself scored a sixth touchdown with a two-point conversion in the first minute of the fourth quarter.

Then the Ravens pushed back, breaking the tie with a daring field goal.

But as the clock was running out, Malina got hold of the ball and made a last-ditch dash to the end zone. "I don't know what happened," he said. "The other guys cleared a path for me and I just kept running. No one hit me. I ran and ran until I heard everyone shouting. Then I realized I had made it!" Malina had made a seventy-five-yard run to win the game, with a final score of 50-46 Eagles.

"I knew Malina was good for the team, but I didn't know how good," Coach Wilson said. "All the boys on the field helped

The Ravens played hard, but the Eagles managed to upset them.

him make that run, and Malina knows it. He had the ball in his hands, but everyone made that touchdown."

This is the first time GHS has made it to the finals in sixteen years. Coach Wilson says he hopes that will become a tradition. The final game is on Saturday at 2:00 P.M. ❖

Eagles Marching Band Nabs Four Trophies

The marching band won best overall performance in the state, as well as three other firsts.

It's time to toot our own horn, Greenville! The Eagles Marching Band returned from a trip to a statewide band competition today with four trophies. In addition to winning best overall performance, the band won for best drum line, best drum majors, and best drill **choreography**.

Maria Saad, band director

"We are very proud of the kids," said Maria Saad, the band's director, via telephone after the awards ceremony last night. "They worked hard, performed well, and acted professionally the whole time. They were a good group to travel with."

The band left during the school day last Friday. Many students gathered in front of the school to send off the three buses.

After spending most of the day on the road, the group had only one night of rest before the competitions began.

Competitions were held in the football arena of State University. Roughly twenty-five high school bands were in attendance, so the stands were full the entire time. Each band performed once on each of the days. The first day was dedicated to traditional marches; the second day was

The Eagles Marching Band has become the pride of Greenville.

band's choice. The Eagles performed a **medley** of beloved John Philip Sousa marches, as well as a few well-known hits by the classic '60s/'70s R&B band Kool & The Gang, including "Jungle Boogie" and "Celebration."

Though the Eagles band was confident, the competition was

Director Saad knew her band was nervous, so she reminded them that they were there to have fun. "Winning is nice," she said, "but as long as we were having fun and doing our best, I didn't care if we took home a trophy."

The relaxation technique paid off. "We were on fire!" Ramirez said. "I've never seen us march like that. We were totally in sync."

The awards ceremony yesterday evening turned out to be a wonderful experience for the group. Much to their surprise, they took home four trophies. "They just kept calling us to the podium!" Saad said. "Award after award, we kept winning."

stiff. According to tenth-grade drum major Raquel Ramirez, "Some of the bands on the field were just amazing. They played perfectly, they marched perfectly. There was even another drum major who did flips along the sideline. I was really intimidated."

This is the first time the Eagles marching band has won at the state level. Though it is still early to make travel plans, they do expect to compete again next year. ❖

Analyze the Information in the Articles

- What are the articles about?

- What do the three articles have in common?

- The writer uses direct quotes to support her stories. Identify two for each article.

- How do direct quotes help you understand the information in each article?

- How does each article end?

Focus on Comprehension: Summarize Information

- Write a three- to four-sentence summary for each article. Be sure to include who, what, when, where, why, and how in your summary.

- In one sentence, summarize how students felt about the locker-room pranks.

- What ideas would you include in a one-sentence summary about Coach Wilson's opinion about Henry Malina?

Analyze the Tools Writers Use: A Strong Lead

Look at the lead in the "Marching Band" article.

- What type of lead does the writer use in this story?

- Does the lead hook you as a reader? Why?

- What do you expect to learn after reading the lead?

Focus on Words: Advanced Nouns

Make a chart like the one below. Reread each sentence containing the advanced noun and determine its definition. Then identify an easier version of each noun that you might use if you were writing a book aimed at second graders.

Page	Word	Definition	Easier Word
6	caper		
7	mascot		
7	mannequin		
9	culprit		
10	conversion		
13	choreography		
14	medley		

School Council Presidential Race Neck and Neck

News articles are published in a timely way. This article is for morning readers to learn about something that will happen that afternoon and the next day. It is an example of a hard news story.

News writers often interview people they call sources to get information or quotes. Good sources are experts on the topic, or people who witnessed an event firsthand.

The final day before the School Council elections has reached fever pitch! **Front-runners** for president José Cruz and Alice Chen will make their final speeches this afternoon in the gymnasium during seventh period. This will be the last chance for the **candidates** to speak to the student body before Monday's election.

Cruz and Chen have been working especially hard this past week to win last-minute supporters. Students were greeted on Monday morning with campaign signs tacked to every wall in the school. "They let us come in over the weekend to put the signs up," Chen told *The Greenville Gazette*. "I had a group helping me, and José had his group. We put the signs everywhere we could."

In addition to the signs, the two candidates have been handing out buttons and stickers at the front doors in the morning. Every student at GHS has at least one stuck to his or her backpack. Some students even have one for each candidate. "I like them both, so I can't choose!" tenth-grader Thomas Johnson said. "I think that either one would make a great school council president."

José Cruz

Alice Chen

The main problem facing the candidates now is indecision. It seems that both Cruz and Chen have scored points with their fellow students. In the debate last Friday, Cruz promised "to extend the number of minutes between classes." He said that students need more time to use the restroom and visit their lockers. Chen promised "a better selection of food in the cafeteria." Both candidates agreed on the need for more student **fund-raising**. Cruz wants funds to tune all the school's pianos. Chen would buy some new athletic equipment.

The writer includes information and quotes from both candidates. The writer's job is to give multiple perspectives so that the reader can draw his or her own conclusions.

Polling done after the debate showed the student body is still undecided.

Student Poll Results*

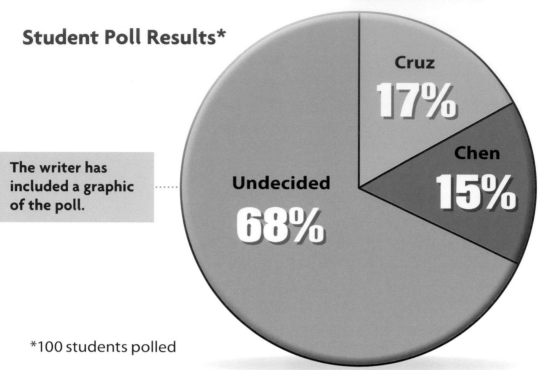

The writer has included a graphic of the poll.

*100 students polled

News writers often quote statistics to confirm or disprove information they are given by sources.

Of a hundred students polled, 15 reported they prefer Chen and 17 prefer Cruz, leaving 68 undecided. When asked why they were undecided, the 68% said they would be happy with either candidate. "I think I'll decide when I'm looking at the ballot," ninth-grader Tamika Herold said. "I've heard both of their plans, and I'll think about it until Monday."

Cruz and Chen hope to make up some minds this afternoon. "I wrote, like, five drafts of my speech," Cruz said. "I think there are many good ideas in it. I hope my fellow students think so, too."

The student body is still largely undecided about the upcoming election.

Chen also hopes to seal the deal today. "I know I would make the best school council president. I have good ideas, and I know I will be able to get things done."

To hear the final speeches, report to the gymnasium at the start of seventh period. Teachers will be giving passes to students who wish to attend. Voting begins Monday at 8:00 A.M. The booths will be set up in the cafeteria until 1:00 P.M. ❖

One of the most important aspects of news writing is making sure people have the information they need to do something, such as when and where they can vote.

Informational texts sometimes describe the history of something or someone.

This kind of story is called a feature. Features are news stories that discuss one topic in great depth. They often are not as timely as news stories and are usually longer.

Weekly Profile: The History of Bob the Orange Blob

A group of students in 1968 created an apple sculpture for the school courtyard.

It's big and blobby, and very orangey. And you see it every day when you walk up to school. But do you know where Bob (the orange blob sculpture in the courtyard) comes from? It turns out the story is as interesting as Bob itself.

In 1968, a group of students approached former art teacher Angela Smith, who retired ten years ago. They wanted to decorate GHS's courtyard. She decided that she could use this opportunity to teach the students sculpture.

"I've always loved sculpture," Smith said from her home in Sarasota, Florida. "But it's hard to teach. You need so much equipment, and it's so BIG. This was the perfect moment to get the school to invest in some supplies."

So the small group of students began work on a sculpture of an apple, a symbol of education. They decided to use steel, so professional sculptors came with equipment to help with the dangerous parts. The students worked for an entire school year until they got the apple perfect.

"We were just about to paint it with the school colors when there was an accident," former student Theodore Wang said. He was one of the students who worked on the project. "One of the hired guys was welding on the stem and leaf, and the whole thing fell off of the base. Everything smashed and broke apart."

The writer hooks the reader with a strong lead that describes something fun and weird.

Feature writers try to interview people who know the topic better than anyone else. This teacher is an ideal primary source since she started the original art project.

Retired art teacher Angela Smith

Feature writers quote exactly how people speak. This adds credibility to the writer and the article.

broken apple sculpture

At the time, the students were disappointed, but still glad they had given it a try and learned new skills. They decided that if it couldn't be a perfect piece of art in the courtyard, it could be a strange piece of art at a rival school. So they planned a prank on Kingston High School.

"On the night before KHS's big football game, my brother helped us load the broken sculpture into the back of our dad's truck," said Sandra Patel, now a local orthodontist. "We drove it over to Kingston, drove up to the football field, and rolled it to the middle."

Kingston football players were surprised when they arrived at the school for practice to find a huge ball of steel at the fifty-yard line. They knew immediately that it had to be a Greenville prank.

A few weeks later, the sculpture—its pieces now welded together—was brought back to Greenville by a group of Kingston students and parents. (Again, it was the middle of the night.) They then welded it in place at the site in the courtyard that had been set up for the piece.

The writer is using logical organization to tell the history of Bob. She is using sequence indicators such as "a few weeks later," "the next morning," and "a few years later."

When everyone arrived at school the next morning, the sculpture was the hot topic of conversation. And, surprisingly, the students liked it. "They all said it looked modern and cool," Wang remembered. "So, the school decided to leave it."

A few years later, former principal Thomas Brown noticed a serious problem. "Birds did

Students circa 1976 painted Bob orange at the request of Principal Brown, who read that the color wards off birds.

their business all over it!" he said. "Not only was it gross, it was damaging the metal." He read an article about sculptors who paint their work orange to ward off birds. He decided to give it a try, and the brightly painted object became known as Bob the Orange Blob.

"I don't know where I read that article," Brown admits, "but it was certainly not true. The birds still love to hang out on Bob. Students have to repaint it every year."

Current art teacher Jamal Whitestone is in charge of keeping Bob in good shape. "Some people have suggested changing the color a few times, but the rest of us think Bob is too distinctive to change. It's like a second mascot for our school," he said.

Even though features are not always timely, they are often published at a time when people are interested in a certain topic. Since the redesign of the school courtyard just happened, people would be interested in the history of Bob.

Last year, the school decided to renovate the courtyard and parking lot to make more spaces. The original redesign removed the blob and placed it in the yard behind the school. That plan was immediately and unanimously rejected. In the **transcript** of the design review meeting, the school board said that Bob was too distinctive, too historical, and too much a part of the school community to remove. The final design **proposal**, accepted last month, neatly works around the sculpture.

According to Principal Lakhi, everyone should know the history of the art they walk past every day. "It's really important to remember why the school is the way it is," she said. "Besides, Bob is part of our community, even if he is blobby." ❖

The writer concludes with an ending that will make the reader think about Bob (and smile) the next time he or she passes it in the school courtyard.

Students today continue a school tradition by painting Bob orange every year.

Analyze the Information in the Articles

• What are the articles about?

• What do the two articles have in common?

• The writer uses direct quotes to support the stories. Identify two for each article.

• How do direct quotes help you understand the information in each article?

• How does each article end?

Focus on Comprehension: Summarize Information

• Write a three- to four-sentence summary for each article. Be sure to include who, what, when, where, why, and how in your summary.

• In one sentence, summarize how students feel about each candidate.

• What ideas would you include in a one-sentence summary about how people at the school feel about Bob the Orange Blob?

Focus on Catchy Titles

News writers include strong leads in their informational articles. But what about titles? Titles are just as important, if not more so, than strong leads because they catch the reader's eye before the lead. That is why good titles are referred to as "catchy" titles. Reread the titles of the last two articles. What about the titles catches your attention? What did you think the articles were going to be about?

Analyze the Tools Writers Use: A Strong Lead

Look at the leads in these articles.

• What type of lead does the writer use in each story?
• Do the leads hook you as a reader? Why?
• What do you expect to learn after reading the leads?

Focus on Words: Advanced Nouns

Make a chart like the one below. Reread each sentence containing the advanced noun and determine its definition. Then identify an easier version for each noun that you might use if you were writing a book aimed at second graders.

Page	Word	Definition	Easier Word
18	front-runners		
18	candidates		
19	fund-raising		
26	transcript		
26	proposal		

How does an author write an
Informational Text?

Reread "The History of Bob the Orange Blob" and think about what Rebecca Grudzina did to write this informational text. How did she keep a narrow focus? How did she help you understand the text?

❶ Decide on a Topic

Choose something you are interested in and want to know more about. Good writers enjoy researching their topics.

❷ Narrow Your Focus

Rebecca Grudzina knew she couldn't write everything there is to know about Greenville High School, so she narrowed her focus to the history of the sculpture in the courtyard of the school.

❸ Write a Question About Your Focus

Questions lead to answers, so turn your focus into a question.

❹ Research Your Focus

Become the "expert" by reading articles on the Internet, reading books and newspaper articles, and interviewing people connected with your topic. (For instance, Rebecca interviewed the art teacher who helped the students make Bob.) You want to show readers that you know what you are talking about.

❺ Organize Your Information

Before writing an informational article, make a chart or table like the one on the next page that outlines the main points. For each main point, identify supporting details. You don't have to write full sentences. These are your notes. Remember, however, that there should be a logical progression of ideas.

⑥ Write Your Informational Text

As you write, develop each main point with your supporting details. Remember, you want people to enjoy reading your article as well as learn something new.

Topic: Greenville High School

Focus: History of Bob the Orange Blob

Question: What is the history of Bob the Orange Blob?

Main Point	Details
Audience	Bob is something students see every day.
	Most students do not know where Bob came from.
The Idea Behind the Blob	In 1968, students asked art teacher Angela Smith to help them decorate the courtyard.
	The class decided to make an apple sculpture.
How the Apple Became a Blob	The apple fell as a professional sculptor was welding it.
What Happened Next?	As a prank, GHS students moved Bob to KHS.
	KHS students and parents welded Bob, then put it back in place in the GHS courtyard.
How Bob Became Orange	Birds did their business on it.
	The principal read an article about orange paint preventing that.
Bob Now	Bob is part of the school's identity.
	The new courtyard and parking lot design plan was rejected because it meant moving Bob.

Glossary

candidates (KAN-dih-dates) people seeking office or an award (page 18)

caper (KAY-per) a prank or theft (page 6)

choreography (kor-ee-AH-gruh-fee) an arrangement of movements, usually for a performance (page 13)

conversion (kun-VER-zhun) a point or points earned in football after a touchdown (page 10)

culprit (KUL-prit) the source or cause of a problem or crime (page 9)

front-runners (FRUNT-ruh-nerz) leading contestants in a race (page 18)

fund-raising (FUND-ray-zing) collecting money for a cause or organization (page 19)

mannequin (MA-nih-kin) a human-shaped dummy used to display clothing (page 7)

mascot (MAS-kaht) a good-luck charm or costumed character for a team, school, or other organization (page 7)

medley (MED-lee) a musical composition made from a series of songs (page 14)

proposal (pruh-POH-zul) a suggested plan, often submitted to a committee (page 26)

transcript (TRAN-skript) a written record of what was said (page 26)